the Desert Underground

By Robin Kobaly

Exposing a Valuable Hidden World Under Our Feet

Researched and written by Robin Kobaly

Original art by Dr. Juniper Harrower

The SummerTree Institute
Making Environmental Education Irresistible

First Edition
Published September 2019
The SummerTree Institute
Morongo Valley, California

the Desert Underground

Exposing a Valuable Hidden World Under Our Feet

You are invited on a tour of our desert underground, a hidden world of incredibly deep, ancient, plant roots living in partnership with a diverse population of microbes, together accomplishing feats of chemical transformation that delight scientists. What is happening in our desert soils may sound like science fiction, but be assured that everything you are about to see and read here is documented science.

Few people have been on a tour of this surprising underground realm that affects everything which happens above the ground. Tiny but powerful microscopic organisms drive a natural system that makes our home a better, healthier place to live.

Although mostly invisible, these microorganisms keep the soil glued together, prevent dust storms, hold dangerous particulate matter and harmful fungal spores tight in the soil so we do not breathe them into our lungs, and perhaps most importantly store vast amounts of carbon underground.

Large-scale construction projects, such as utility-scale solar facilities, cause major disruption of surface soils and vegetation. What is often overlooked during even the most rigorous consideration of these projects is the significant impact that these activities cause underground. We disregard these impacts at our own peril. Vegetation removal and soil destruction halt every functional system of life that had been working for us—and impact everything that happens above the ground.

During this tour, you will see what happens when our desert soil is disturbed and how that disturbance affects people both near the site of the disturbance and many miles away. Massive soil-disrupting projects impact our air quality, our soil stability, our landscape, our carbon sequestration capability, our quality of life, and our future. The potential damage caused when we disrupt valuable desert soils should encourage us to site any future large-scale developments in our southwest deserts only on areas of pre-disturbed, severely impacted soils or pre-developed sites such as parking lots and rooftops.

Protecting pristine and naturally functioning desert soils protects more than just those soils. It protects our own health today and every day, long into the future, and contributes to the health of our planet.

Incredible things are happening in our desert soils that may sound like science fiction, but be assured that everything you are about to see here is documented science.

Few people have ever taken a tour of this surprising underground realm that affects our world every day.

Ancient Plants Regulate our Landscape

The anchors of any community are often individuals that have resided there longest, whether they are humans, animals, or plants. The anchors of our natural desert community, those contributing the most to the long-range viability of the entire landscape, happen to be the longest lived of any of the denizens here: our extremely long-lived native plants.

These plants grow under extremely harsh conditions, including long droughts, drying winds, intense sun, punishing heat, and nutrient-poor soils. Because of these challenges, these plants can only survive by growing slowly and deliberately, conserving energy at all cost. They put most of their growth efforts downward into the soil to build a foundation with no frivolous or lush growth that would squander their precious water and resources.

These adaptations have resulted in extremely long lives. It is this achievement that makes these plants so critical to the long-term health of our southwest ecosystem.

The ages of our native desert plants may astound you, especially because a plant only three or four feet tall may be many centuries old. Small shrubs like Blackbrush can live at least 400 years, while Mormon Tea can live over 250 years. Our bunch grasses like Galleta Grass live at least 100 years, and our Cholla cactus can live several hundred years.

Our Mojave Yuccas are youngsters at 500 years old, and may live to several thousand years old. Pinyon Pines can live over 500 years, our Scrub Oaks over 800 years, and Nolinas and Desert Ironwood trees likely live well over 1,000 years. California Junipers may live over 1,000 years also.

Creosote bushes are the oldest of them all. A one-foot-tall Creosote bush may already be at least ten years old and usually more. The average age of Creosote bushes across our landscape here is likely about 600 to 1,000 years old, but many individual bushes are undoubtedly well over 1,000 years old. One of the oldest Creosote bushes studied to date, still living in Johnson Valley, is estimated to be at least 10,000 years old.

What do these long lives mean to us and to our desert? They translate into living links that sustain life across centuries of drought episodes, excessive heat waves, frosts that kill younger plants, and onslaughts of diseases or pests that compromise young plants struggling to become established. Over centuries, the old, mature plants have developed extensive root systems, concentrations of chemical weapons in their tissues, and dense, hard, durable stems and trunks to stand up to attacks by diseases, herbivory, pests, droughts, freezes, and most other threats. However, one thing they cannot survive is bulldozers.

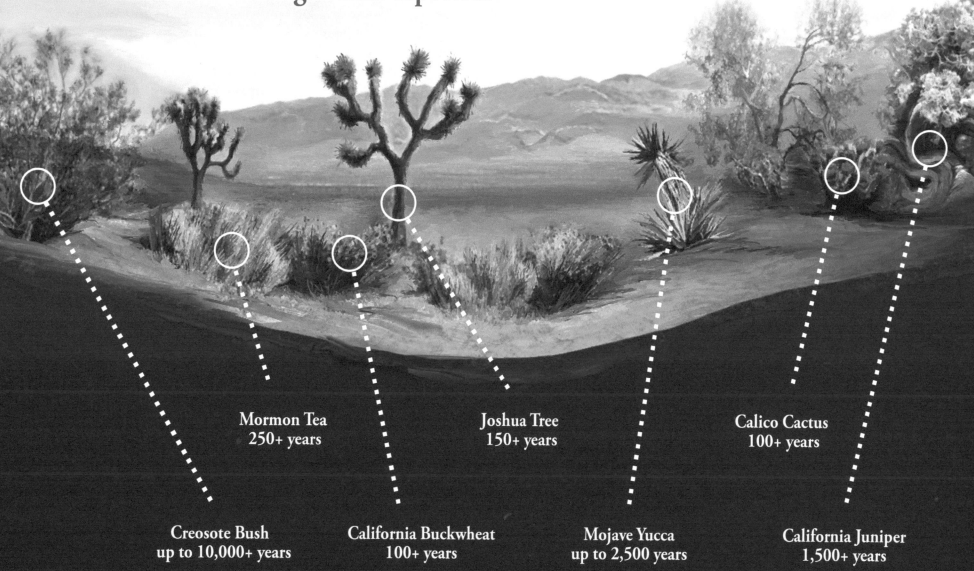

This tour starts above the ground with plants that live far longer than expected.

Mormon Tea
250+ years

Joshua Tree
150+ years

Calico Cactus
100+ years

Creosote Bush
up to 10,000+ years

California Buckwheat
100+ years

Mojave Yucca
up to 2,500 years

California Juniper
1,500+ years

Underground Systems Drive Aboveground Life

When we look across the desert landscape, the portion of our native vegetation that we see above the ground is very deceptive in respect to the total picture. The desert's mostly dwarf-looking plants only look small above the ground; however, below the ground their roots can extend to surprising depths in their quest to find moisture.

Underground, unseen events are constantly reshaping the world beneath our feet. Rather than the soil being filled simply with plant roots, much more is happening at different soil depths, and it affects us all. What we see at the surface of the desert is a tiny portion of what makes the desert "tick." Each level of soil contains something critical which affects the aboveground world we live in.

At the surface, a living layer of microscopic algae, fungus, and bacteria binds the soil surface together. This layer of living soil is known by several names including biological soil crust, cryptogamic soil, cryptobiotic crust, microbiotic crust, and other names. Here we will refer to it as biological soil crust, or "biocrust." This biocrust is attracting the focus of scientists around the world who study drylands.

Below the surface, extremely long plant roots grow at least two times to a dozen times longer than what we see growing above the ground (succulent plants like cacti and yuccas are an exception, having shallower roots and a different strategy for absorbing water from the soil). A one-foot-tall Creosote bush, for example, already has at least three feet of roots searching deep into the soil for moisture. A six-inch-tall Desert Evening Primrose has roots about five to six feet deep which is almost twelve times longer than the plant is tall.

These deep plant roots grow down to soils that may still contain moisture from rains that fell many years earlier, providing a lifeline to plants that may be experiencing prolonged years of drought. While surface soils may have dried out years earlier, deep soils may still hold moisture available to plants with extremely long roots.

At different soil depths, chunks or layers of hard soil called "caliche" hold carbon underground. The creation of this massive carbon sequestration system will be discussed later on this tour. Caliche is of major importance in the global carbon cycle.

Moving underground, unseen events are constantly reshaping the world beneath our feet.

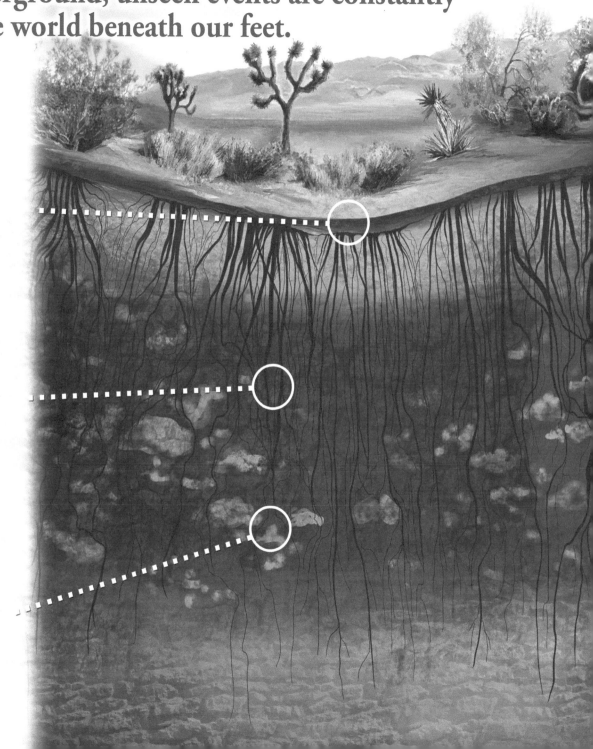

A living layer of microscopic algae, fungus, and bacteria binds the soil surface together.

Extremely deep roots grow 2 to 10+ times as deep as the plant is tall. These deep roots transfer carbon from the air down into the soil.

Chunks or layers of cemented soil called "caliche" capture and hold carbon underground.

Native Plants and Soil Microbes Join Forces

Our desert plants and soil microbes work together to:

Prevent dust storms by binding soil grains tightly together so wind can't pick up dust and soil

Make living glue that binds soil particles together, preventing wind and water erosion

Hold dangerous particulate matter in the soil so we do not breath it, preventing possible damage to lungs and human health

Capture and store carbon underground in living systems – even after these organisms die if the soil is not disturbed

Capture and store carbon underground in caliche – for thousands of years if the soil is not disturbed

Both above and below the soil surface, plants and soil microorganisms work to help each other survive, and the result is very beneficial to humans and the entire ecosystem.

Our desert plants and soil microbes work together to:

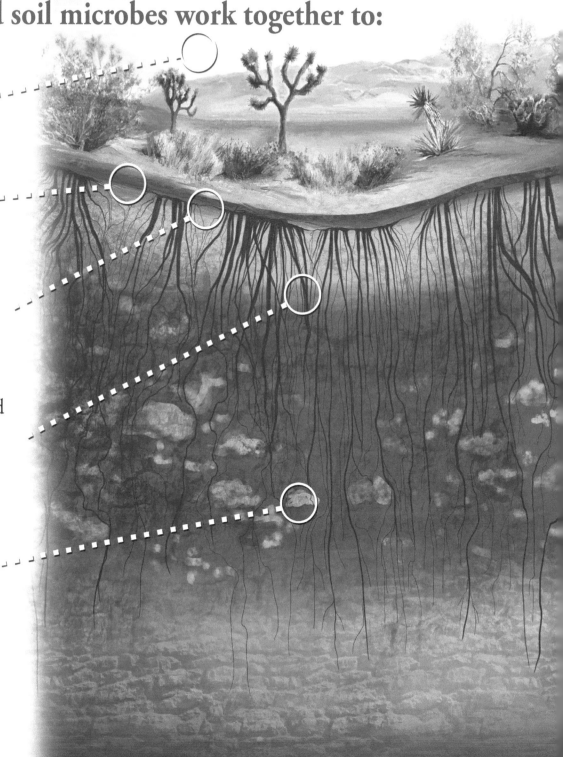

Prevent dust storms

Make living glue that binds soil particles together

Hold dangerous particulate matter in the soil so we don't breathe it

Capture and store carbon underground in living systems – even after they die if the soil isn't disturbed

Capture and store carbon underground in caliche for thousands of years – if the soil isn't disturbed

Biological Soil Crusts Stabilize our Soil

A thin surface crust forms across arid soils on or within the top few centimeters of the soil surface. Surprisingly, these crusts are not made up simply of encrusted, excess soil minerals as often thought, but are created by microscopic and somewhat larger macroscopic organisms that live together in an under-appreciated but profound world.

Whenever it rains, a cast of soil creatures (including cyanobacteria, formerly called blue-green algae, plus bacteria, fungi, and other microbes) that have been patiently sleeping wakes up like a scene from Sleeping Beauty's castle. Released from the spell of drought, these microscopic creatures start making food and creating miniature, slimy subway tunnels as they move through the soil, reproducing as long as the soil is moist. Tunnels of sticky mucilage around algae filaments allow the algae to move into new frontiers while moisture paves their way.

As these microscopic creatures move through the top several inches of what appears to be lifeless soil, they create a tenacious soil glue through their tunneling activity. As the soil dries out after rain, a slumber again falls over the entire community, and the soft, gooey tunnels they formed start to dry out – but not before tightly binding together all the soil grains they have touched. The value of this thin, living "skin" across our desert soil is not only expressed during its wet "waking hours," but also during its dry, dormant time.

During the coming months or years of drought, these sticky tunnels continue to bind soil grains together against the fierce winds that try to pry loose any soil that is not secured by these glue-like transportation threads. Even when dry, this living crust performs the critical role of keeping dust and dirt from polluting the air.

These microbes live only near the top few centimeters of the soil because they need sunlight to grow and make their own food. Wherever they travel, their network of mucilaginous, hollow tunnels between soil grains records a history of their movements and leaves a lasting legacy of soil cohesion.

These living soil crusts take hundreds of years to develop into effective soil sealants. When they are allowed to remain intact, they will hold back wind and water erosion, supply nutrients to neighboring plants, improve water infiltration, prevent particulate matter from entering the air, and help keep our air clean and healthy. Plus, they do all this for us while they are sleeping.

These and other tiny microbes living between our soil grains create and store scarce, valuable, fertilizing nutrients like phosphorus and nitrogen below the surface, and they share these building blocks for life with all the plants in the surrounding community. If not disturbed by vehicle wheels or bulldozer blades, this soil "living glue" and the community that produced it can persist for many thousands of years—or more.

Let's look closer, starting from the top:

Microscopic algae, fungi, and bacteria live in our surface soils, and sleep during droughts. Rain wakes them up. As they move through the soil, they make gooey "subway tunnels" around themselves.

As the soil dries out after rain, their tunnels become a very effective "living glue" that tightly binds soil together.

These living surface soils are called "biological soil crusts," or biocrusts.

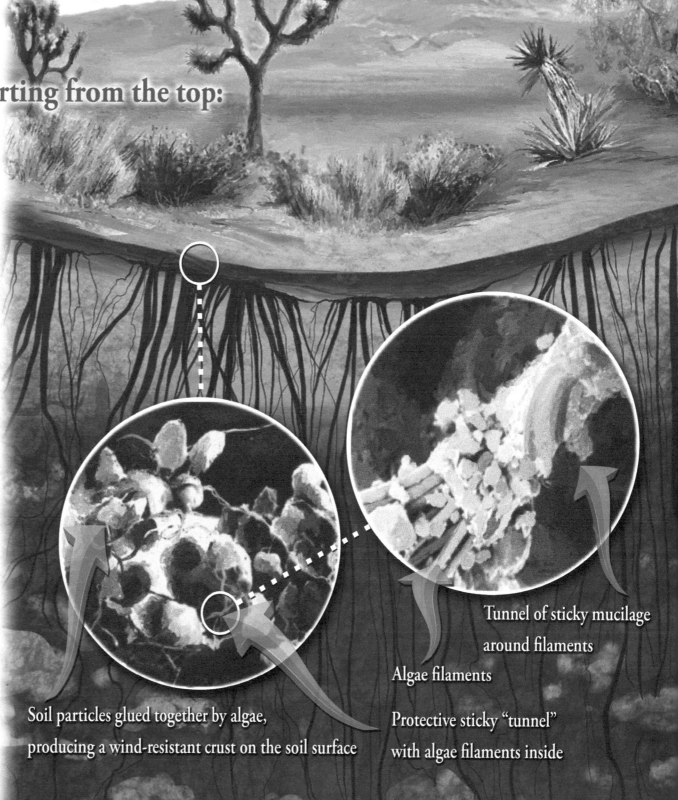

Soil particles glued together by algae, producing a wind-resistant crust on the soil surface

Tunnel of sticky mucilage around filaments

Algae filaments

Protective sticky "tunnel" with algae filaments inside

Biological Soil Crusts Prevent Dust Storms

Biological soil crusts keep soils intact and prevent dust storms…unless soils are disturbed. The dried, glue-like threads of microbes in biocrusts form a resistant seal across the soil surface, keeping dust, particulate matter, and harmful fungal spores like valley fever from being blown up into the air wherever the soil has not been disturbed.

The tiny particles of pollution known as particulate matter (PM) are the subject of intense research related to human health. PM particles include larger particles like dust, dirt, smoke, and soot that we can see, and smaller particles that are microscopic. Two main categories of particulate matter occur in our air and soil: PM2.5 and PM10. Each number represents the diameter of particles in a measurement called microns. PM10 particles are smaller than 10 microns, less than the width of a single human hair. PM2.5 particles are so small they can penetrate our lungs and enter our bloodstream.

When living soil crusts are disturbed, particulate matter is dislodged, and choking dust storms occur. Dust storms blow harmful particulate matter into the air – and we breathe it in.

PM10 particles inhaled into our lungs cause health impacts ranging from coughing and wheezing to asthma attacks and bronchitis, as well as high blood pressure, heart attacks, strokes, and premature death in people with heart and lung issues.

Even smaller particles, PM2.5's (created by combustion), are being recorded in our desert dust storms. While PM10's can lodge in our lungs when inhaled, PM2.5's can pass from our lungs into our blood supply and be carried throughout our bodies, causing even more severe health issues.

Dust storms can also carry dangerous valley fever spores from soil into the air, causing serious lung infections.

Look across the desert when you see dust storms. You will notice that dust storms start over disturbed soils and rarely originate from landscapes with intact soils around native plants in undisturbed habitat.

Biological soil crusts keep soils intact and prevent dust storms ...

unless soils are disturbed.

When living soil crusts are disturbed, choking dust storms occur.

Dust storms blow harmful particulate matter smaller than 10 microns (PM10's) into the air – and we breathe it in.

Dust storms can blow dangerous valley fever spores from soil into the air, causing serious lung infections.

Dust storm occurring over disturbed soil. Microscopic particles, PM10's, are blown into the air from disturbed soil, creating serious health hazards when breathed in.

PM10's inhaled into our lungs cause health impacts including coughing, wheezing, bronchitis, asthma attacks, high blood pressure, heart attacks, strokes, and premature death in people with heart and lung issues.

Plants and Fungi Unite to Form an Underground "Internet"

All the deep plant roots underground are not separate and alone in their quest to gather water and nutrients to survive. Eons ago, plants struck upon a partnership with fungus that helps them absorb moisture and nutrients from arid soils that can be almost devoid of either. Over 90% of plants on earth belong to this "Root Partners' Club," a lifelong membership that grants participating plants special privileges.

The plant host benefits from allowing a network of fungus to grow into or around their roots by receiving a super-injected flow of critical nutrients, water, pest-deterring compounds, and even immune-boosting chemicals from the fungus.

These valuable resources are all gathered and brought to the plants by thin threads of fungal hyphae that have spread far and wide to find, retrieve, absorb, and deliver these scarce treasures to their attached plant partner.

In exchange, the plant host supplies sugars they have made to their fungal root partner, which, for all their near-magical powers, cannot make their own food. This is a good trade indeed.

The root system of fungi, called mycelium, not only connects to plant roots, but also interconnects all roots to each other like nature's internet. This creates a virtual "Wood Wide Web" underground and allows plants to communicate and share resources and information with each other.

Going still deeper, plant roots are connected in partnership with special fungi:

Plants need help to absorb water and nutrients from desert soils lacking in both.

Fungi are the best sponges in the world at absorbing moisture and nutrients ... but they can't make food.

Plants will share their "food" (sugars and carbs) if fungi share the resources they have gathered -- a good trade. This partnership has been called a "subterranean swap meet."

Fungi grow hyphae into or around plant roots to deliver nutrients and water to them; plants reward the fungus by sharing the sugars they make.

The root system of fungi, called mycelium, connects to plant roots, and interconnects all roots to each other like nature's internet ... creating a virtual "Wood Wide Web" underground, and allowing plants to communicate and share with each other.

Mushrooms are the "Tip of The Mycelium"

Most of the body of the fungal root partner remains underground, unseen but providing enormous benefits to plants in the community. Occasionally, when conditions are right, the mycelium of some types of fungi produce spore-filled reproductive structures that we know as mushrooms. These mushrooms push up through the ground, seeking air to spread their spores.

There is more to this relationship than sharing resources. The thin threads from the ever-searching, ever-growing fungal root partner form a three-dimensional lace or "doily" underground that not only connects to its chosen plant host, but also to all the fungal partners connected to all the plants in the community. They form a true network of communication that keeps all plants in a community "talking" to each other, sharing resources when necessary, and alerting each other of dangers.

Without seeing anything above the ground, the fungal hyphae below the ground inform the whole community of dangers like insect attacks and initiate the production of pest-repelling compounds to all plants connected to this network.

The root system of fungi is made of thread-like hyphae called "mycelium."

Artistic view of mushroom above the ground, attached to its mycelium below the ground. Think of a 3-dimensional lace or doily spreading underground.

Plant root with white mycelium attached

Mycorrhizae: A Strategic Partnership Between Plants and Fungi

The relationship between a host plant and a root-partnering fungus is called "mycorrhizal." This term literally means "fungus-root," from the Latin and Greek words for fungus, "myco," and root, "rhiza." Most of our plants on earth are mycorrhizal, which means they have a partner-forming, mutually beneficial relationship, or symbiosis, with fungi.

The root-like hyphae (the collective mass being called mycelium) of root-partnering fungi connect to the actively absorbing roots of their plant host. The mycelium grows outward from the plant's roots in all directions to search out and retrieve moisture and nutrients, delivering much of their collected gatherings back to their plant host.

The prolific mycelium can effectively expand the absorbing surface area of the plant's roots by up to 700 percent or more. In exchange for this service, the plant may share with its fungal partner about 10 to 20 percent of the food it creates or collects (including valuable products like carbohydrates/sugars, vitamins, and amino acids). In the end, the plant may realize over 100 times the value of its investment.

Besides delivering nutrients and moisture to their plant hosts, mycorrhizal fungi may speed plant growth, extend the lifespan of roots, and protect host plants from drought, predators, and pathogens such as microorganisms that cause disease.

The underground diversity of mycorrhizal fungi (lots of different species of fungi) is a major factor that contributes to the aboveground diversity of plants in an ecosystem. To protect a broad array of plant species aboveground, therefore, we need to conserve the mycorrhizal fungal diversity in the soil.

Some fungi produce mushrooms aboveground under certain conditions. The mushroom you see is the fruiting body of a fungus, growing up through the soil from the mycelium underground. The fruiting bodies that break through the soil to spread their spores are called mushrooms or toadstools, while some of those that remain below the ground we commonly call truffles.

The relationship between a host plant and the mycelium of a root-partnering fungi is called "mycorrhizal."

Over 90 percent of all plants on earth are mycorrhizal, or have a partner-forming symbiosis with fungi.

The mycelium of root-partnering fungi connect to plant roots and may produce mushrooms above the ground.

Plant root (orange)

Fungal mycelium (white)

Roots of plant host   Mycelium of fungus

To See or Not To See Mushrooms: That is the Question

All mycorrhizal fungi have networks of hyphae called mycelium, but not all produce mushrooms above the ground. Some produce spore bodies that remain underground, so their presence remains hidden to us.

Two main types of mycorrhizal fungi occur in our deserts, one type producing mushrooms, the other keeping its fruiting bodies hidden underground:

> *Ecto*mycorrhizal fungi grow around plant roots; these produce mushrooms to spread spores aboveground. Desert plants sharing this type of mycorrhizal relationship include pinyon pine, scrub oak, and manzanita.

> *Endo*mycorrhizal fungi grow inside plant roots; these don't produce mushrooms. Their spores stay underground. Desert plants that share this type of relationship include creosote bush, jojoba, cactus, mesquite, Joshua tree, and saltbush.

Most of our desert plant species have partnerships with endomycorrhizal fungi, so we don't see mushrooms to indicate where most mycorrhizal partnerships are living in the desert…but they are there!

Two main types of mycorrhizal fungi occur in our deserts:

***Ecto*mycorrhizal fungi** – grow around plant roots; they produce mushrooms

***Endo*mycorrhizal fungi** – grow inside plant roots; they do not produce mushrooms

Over 90 percent of our desert plant species have partnerships with endomycorrhizal fungi … so we don't see mushrooms to indicate most of our mycorrhizal partnerships in the desert … but they are there!

Endomycorrhizal fungi don't produce mushrooms

Ectomycorrhizal fungi produce mushrooms to spread spores above the ground

All mycorrhizal fungi have networks of hyphae called mycelium, but not all produce aboveground mushrooms. Some produce spore bodies that remain below the ground.

Not all Mushrooms are Mycorrhizal: Some Fend for Themselves

Not every mushroom that you may find is growing in partnership with a living plant. Many mushrooms are the product of fungi that search out and decompose dead plants and animals.

Fungi that "eat" dead matter are called saprophytes. They do not connect to plant roots, so they are not mycorrhizal. As the mycelium encounter dead matter, they break down the debris to create rich new soil, and recycle the carbon, nitrogen, and other essential elements to absorb themselves or release them into the soil.

We eat many saprophytic mushrooms (but some are poisonous). Examples of edible saprophytic mushrooms include oyster, maitake, lion's mane, shiitake, turkey tail, shaggy mane, reishi, and morels.

Saprophytic mushrooms occur scattered singly or in groups where dead organic matter occurs.

Mycorrhizal mushrooms are usually growing in an arc or ring around a plant, and emerge under the drip line of a plant (under the outer branch tips), where the actively growing roots of the plant are growing.

Fungi that "eat" dead matter are called saprophytes.

They do not connect to plant roots, so they are not mycorrhizal.

Coprinus, a saprophytic mushroom, that eats decaying organic matter

Examples of saprophytic mushrooms: oyster, maitake, lion's mane, shiitake, morels

Plants' Breathing Provides Oxygen for Humans Breathing

Animals and humans breathe in the oxygen that plants produce, while plants breathe in the carbon dioxide that animals and humans produce. Plants do not exclusively breathe in carbon dioxide, however. Where they breathe out carbon dioxide is very beneficial to humans.

Plants operate differently above and below the ground and this has major implications for human life. Leaves breathe in carbon dioxide aboveground … taking in carbon from the air (in the light). Roots breathe out carbon dioxide below the ground … and deposit carbon into the ground (in the dark).

Our desert soils store this carbon underground in a variety of ways. Since we have a serious problem of too much carbon in our atmosphere, plants help to combat this problem.

Plants breathe in massive amounts of carbon dioxide from the air, reassembling the carbon into sugar, then transporting it underground to grow more roots. Byproducts from this growth (photosynthesis) become locked in hidden carbon storage vaults underground, both living and non-living, for hundreds to thousands of years.

Our long-lived native plants across the desert landscape are valuable ancient assets to our ecosystem and to us because individual plants can capture carbon out of thin air for multiple centuries or millennia and deposit it underground.

Quick peek above the ground:

Plants operate differently above and below the ground, and this has major implications for human life.

Leaves **breathe in** carbon dioxide aboveground … taking in carbon from the air (in the light).

Roots **breathe out** carbon dioxide below the ground … and deposit carbon into the ground (in the dark).

We have a serious problem of too much carbon in our air.

Plants help combat this problem.

Strategic Partnership Between Plants and Fungi Captures Carbon

Roots from these carbon-eating plants share some of their carbon-containing sugars with their underground fungal partners, moving carbon from the atmosphere into symbiotic soil microbes.

Below the ground, plant roots are respiring, breathing out carbon dioxide just as humans do. Right at the point where a tiny fungal thread connects to the plant root, both the root and the fungus are breathing out carbon dioxide (remember, plants breathe in carbon in the light, and breathe out carbon in the dark, underground).

Some of the carbon dioxide exhaled by roots and fungi reacts with calcium in the soil to form crystals of calcium carbonate, or what is called caliche. Carbon in these crystals becomes locked into the soil.

Looking even closer at the root zone, something critical happens where fungi and roots connect:

Where they meet, roots and fungal partners are both breathing out carbon dioxide.

This breath combines with calcium in the soil, creating crystals of calcium carbonate, or "caliche."

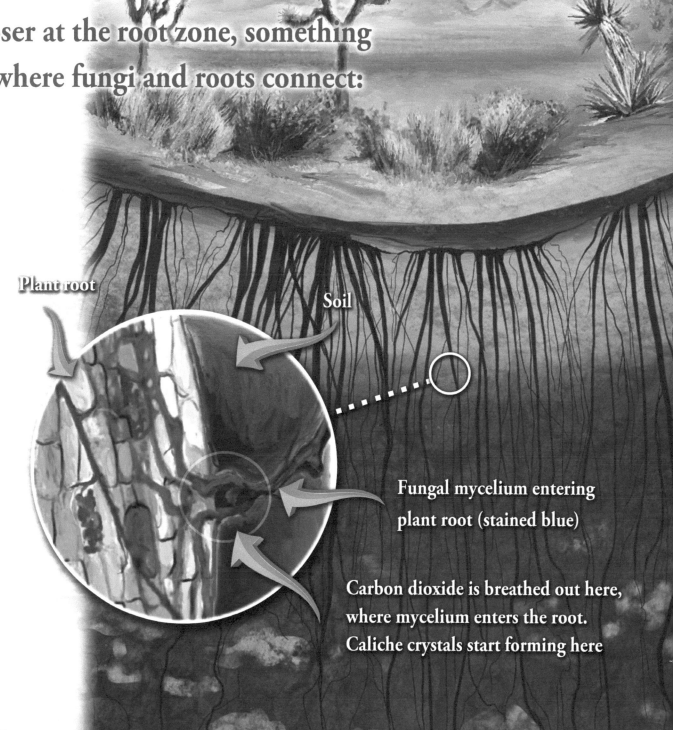

Plant root

Soil

Fungal mycelium entering plant root (stained blue)

Carbon dioxide is breathed out here, where mycelium enters the root. Caliche crystals start forming here

Together Plants and Fungi Sequester Carbon in Caliche

A microscopic view of the point where a single fungal hyphae enters its plant root-partner reveals the formation of a tiny crystal of calcium carbonate, or caliche.

This is the start of what can become larger crystals, and eventually can become layers of caliche, storing captured carbon in the soil.

This tiny crystal formation may seem insignificant, but it results in extremely vast amounts of carbon dioxide being stored in desert soils as caliche.

"Our deserts have large amounts of carbon dioxide stored as caliche. The amount of carbon in caliche, when accounted globally, may be equal to the entire amount of carbon as carbon dioxide in the atmosphere."

– **Dr. Michael Alan**, UCR Center for

Conservation Biology, in *"Solar Power*

in the Desert: Are the current large-scale

solar developments really improving

California's environment?"

Here's what carbon capture looks like under a microscope ... the moment it starts.

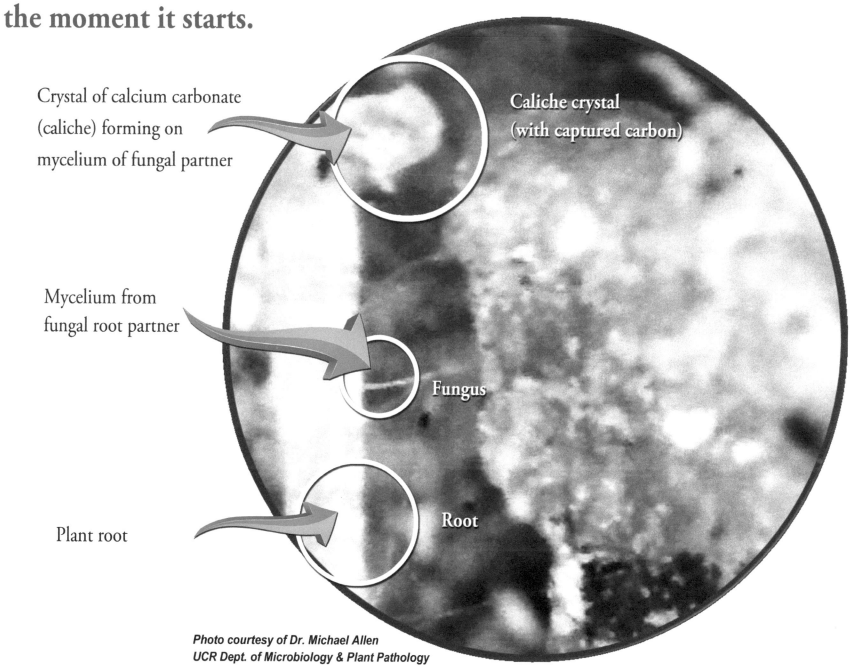

Crystal of calcium carbonate (caliche) forming on mycelium of fungal partner

Caliche crystal (with captured carbon)

Mycelium from fungal root partner

Fungus

Plant root

Root

Photo courtesy of Dr. Michael Allen
UCR Dept. of Microbiology & Plant Pathology

Desert Soils Lock Carbon Underground Inside Caliche

The living partnership of plants with fungal root partners creates one of several ways that carbon-storing caliche is formed.

Over time, crystals of caliche form large chunks and eventually extensive layers of a hardened mineral deposit that can cement together gravel, sand, clay, and silt.

These built-up layers of caliche capture carbon from our atmosphere in a veritable underground lock-box, reducing its potential escape into an atmosphere with an increasing load of carbon dioxide, harmful at higher concentrations. This transfer of carbon from air to leaf to root to fungal partner to caliche deposits is one of nature's ways of sequestering carbon and holding it in a safe place.

Most of the caliche in our desert soils was formed during the Pleistocene when the climate produced more dense and productive vegetation. Ancient deposits of caliche hold vast amounts of carbon in our desert. Despite its long-term storage capabilities, sequestered carbon in caliche may be released when vegetation is removed and soils are disturbed.

Soil disturbance has the potential to degrade soils and reduce carbon sequestration capacity of our desert lands. Scientists are currently working to quantify the carbon gains and losses from intact desert soils versus disturbed desert soils. This research will help inform our understanding of carbon cycling on a global scale.

The result of this underground "exhale" of carbon dioxide is the formation of calcium carbonate crystals, or "caliche."

The living partnership of desert plants with fungal root partners creates carbon-storing caliche deposits underground.

This partnership captures and stores vast amounts of carbon underground for hundreds to thousands of years ... if plants remain alive.

Caliche is formed in several ways. One way occurs at the junction of plant roots with their fungal partner, forming crystals, then chunks, and eventually layers of carbon-containing soils.

Desert Soils Hold Carbon Underground Inside Glomalin

There is yet another champion in our soils that is capturing and keeping carbon out of our air. This recently discovered soil component is another result of the partnership between plants and fungi.

Each and every strand of fungal hyphae of the most common plant-partnering fungi in our desert soil (a type of endomycorrhizal fungi called arbuscular mycorrhizal fungi) is coated with a sealant called "glomalin."

Glomalin is a waterproof sealant that prevents nutrients from leaking out of fungal threads during transport. It also makes each thread stronger.

Forming a protective protein/sugar coating around fungal hyphae, glomalin is made from carbon that was first taken up from the atmosphere by the leaves of plants, turned into sugars, and then sent underground to roots…and is ultimately shared with fungal root partners.

Glomalin is made by fungal hyphae using carbon gathered by the plant that is partnering with the fungus. This process moves atmospheric carbon from the air into the soil for long-term storage. In the end, the covering of countless fungal threads may be one of the major stores of carbon in our soil.

There is yet another champion in our soils that is capturing and keeping carbon out of our air:

The covering of every strand of the most common plant-partnering fungi in our desert soil is made of carbon, taken out of the air by plants.

This protective protein/sugar coating around fungal hyphae, called "glomalin," is made from carbon taken from the atmosphere by plant leaves, turned into sugars, and sent underground to the plant's roots.

Glomalin prevents water and nutrients from leaking out of the fungal threads, and gives strength to each thread.

Glomalin, the leak-proof coating on mycelium (stained green)

Photo courtesy of
USDA Agricultural Research Service

Each strand of mycelium is coated with glomalin, made with carbon

Glomalin – Hiding Place for a Third of the World's Carbon

Because there are many miles of this type of fungal hyphae in every cubic foot of soil, there are many miles of carbon-storing glomalin in each undisturbed cubic foot of our soil.

Glomalin stores one-third of the world's soil carbon, which is important for stabilizing our climate.

This dried sealant continues for many decades after death to sequester and hold carbon underground in undisturbed soils across the desert -- helping us in our quest to reduce greenhouse gases in our atmosphere.

Glomalin is causing a complete reexamination of what makes up soil organic matter according to the USDA Agricultural Research Service. Glomalin is increasingly being included in studies of carbon storage and soil quality around the world.

Glomalin has impressive properties that even scientists are tempted to call magical, storing carbon and nitrogen longer than any other soil component and gluing soils together for surprising lengths of time.

New research has found that higher carbon dioxide levels in the air stimulate higher rates of glomalin production and longer fungal hyphae. This indicates that plants joined in fungal partnerships that produce glomalin could become increasingly important for sequestering carbon in a future with higher levels of atmospheric carbon dioxide.

There are many miles of carbon-storing glomalin around fungal hyphae in each undisturbed cubic foot of our soil.

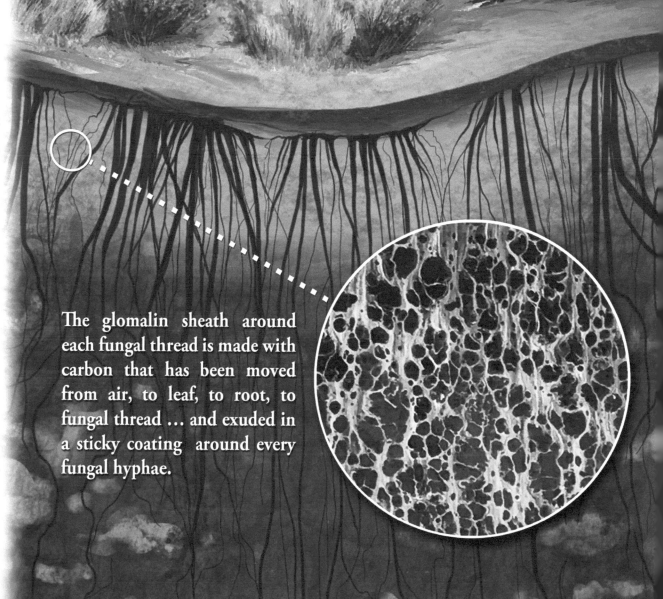

Glomalin stores one-third of the world's soil carbon, important for stabilizing our climate.

Glomalin has impressive properties that even scientists are tempted to call magical, storing carbon and nitrogen longer than any other soil component, and gluing soils together for surprising lengths of time.

The glomalin sheath around each fungal thread is made with carbon that has been moved from air, to leaf, to root, to fungal thread … and exuded in a sticky coating around every fungal hyphae.

Glomalin – Perhaps The Most Important Glue in the World

Glomalin is unique among the world's soil components for its strength and stability. Remarkably, when each fungal filament attached to a root partner dies, its coating of glomalin sloughs off and persists in the soil for 30 to 100 years.

Even after death, glomalin glues soil grains and organic material together, forming clumps. The resulting aggregates of soil are stable enough to resist wind and water erosion yet porous enough to let air, water, and roots move through them.

These soil clumps glued together by glomalin hold carbon, nitrogen, phosphorus, and other valuable nutrients in a netlike packet, preventing them from leaching away and being lost to higher plants that could have taken them up. They also harbor more beneficial microbes, hold more water, and help the soil resist erosion.

Here's how fungal threads bind soil grains together ... with their living glue, "glomalin."

Glomalin has been called ...

"perhaps the most important glue in the world."

Glomalin from each fungal thread can last 30-100 years as a soil glue.

Fungal mycelium

Soil grain held by mycelium

Winds were 15–20 mph when this photograph was taken and no soil grains or aggregates were blown off this chunk of soil.

Plants and Soil Microbes Work Together For Us

If not disturbed by vehicle wheels, bulldozer blades, development, or other soil-disturbing activities, all of these intricate systems continue to work in an ongoing process that constantly replaces itself.

Plants capture carbon and send it underground as they breathe.

The intact living soil crust prevents soil erosion and dust storms every day.

Fungal root partners store carbon in their glomalin coatings that also glue soil together.

Fungal root partners capture carbon in caliche crystals for many thousands of years.

This entire kingdom of incredible creatures works 24 hours a day, year after year, without any input from humans, unseen by us and mostly unappreciated by us. These life forms in mutual partnership will continue to glue our soils together and capture our excess carbon in perpetuity… unless we remove the plants and disturb the soil that makes all this magic continue to work.

We once thought that carbon was held in meaningful amounts only in ocean creatures, forest habitats, and humus (the dark organic matter that forms in soil when dead plant and animal matter decays). Now we know that soils, including desert soils, are also a significant storage facility for carbon.

Not only are desert soils holding carbon in caliche deposits, they also store vast amounts of organic carbon in soil organisms, including root-partnering fungi with their coatings of glomalin. A USDA scientist states the importance of glomalin's carbon storage capacity this way:

"As carbon gets assigned a dollar value in a carbon commodity market, it may give literal meaning to the expression that good soil is black gold. And glomalin could be viewed as its 'golden seal.' "

– **Don Comis**, Agricultural Research

Service, in *"Hiding Place for a Third*

of the World's Stored Soil Carbon"

If not disturbed, all of these intricate systems continue to work in an ongoing process that constantly replaces itself.

Plants capture carbon and send it underground.

The intact living soil crust prevents soil erosion and dust storms every day.

Fungal root partners store carbon in their glomalin coatings that also glue soil together.

Fungal root partners capture carbon in caliche crystals – for many thousands of years.

Desert Soil Disturbance Destroys the Ability of Soils to Prevent Dust Storms and Store Carbon

When soil is scraped and plants are removed, the community of ancient plants dies and their connected underground fungal partners die.

When the soil crust is damaged, all its soil glue breaks up and strong winds pick up the loose grains, dust, and silt, creating dust storms that carry particulate matter up to hundreds or thousands of miles.

Surface erosion impacts are not just local. Impacts can extend for hundreds of yards beyond the disturbance and expand as erosion continues.

If plants are removed, carbon capture ceases. When desert soils are scraped and all vegetation is removed for large-scale projects, sequestered carbon that had been stored is released from various soil depths, from deep to shallow to the surface.

Scientists estimate that the removal of desert vegetation and disturbance of the topsoil requires about 30 years before the pre-existing plant community will begin to grow back; however, it may require about 3,000 years before the disturbed area will return to the function it had before disturbance. The ancient nature of both the plants and the living soil crust organisms make this a credible prediction.

When soil is scraped and plants are removed, the community of ancient plants dies and their connected underground fungal partners die.

When the soil crust is damaged, all its soil glue breaks up and winds pick up the loose grains and silt, creating dust storms that carry particles up to hundreds or thousands of miles.

Surface erosion impacts are not just local. Impacts can extend for hundreds of yards beyond the disturbance and expand as erosion continues.

When plants are removed, carbon capture ceases. Recovery of plants to pre-disturbance cover and biomass may take 50 – 300 years.

Complete ecosystem recovery may require over 3000 years.

Carbon released

When desert soils are scraped and all vegetation is removed for large-scale projects, sequestered carbon that had been stored is released from various soil depths, from deep to shallow to surface.

Disturbed Soils Release Carbon; Intact Soils Sequester Carbon

Scraping off vegetation from an undisturbed desert parcel not only kills all the plants, it kills all the underground fungal root partners attached to those plants that had each been actively sequestering carbon for centuries or millennia.

Without these caliche-forming and glomalin-forming partnerships, significant amounts of carbon are released from the soil back into the atmosphere. Also, no additional carbon is sequestered either by fungi or roots breathing into the soil, or by the growth of carbon-packed glomalin that coats hundreds of miles of fungal hyphae in each pound of soil.

When biological soil crusts are disturbed, their ability to hold soil tightly on the surface is destroyed and choking dust storms occur. Dust storms blow harmful particulate matter and dangerous fungal spores like valley fever into the air – both detrimental to our lungs and health.

We are now faced with decisions about whether to allow thousands of acres of functioning desert systems to be destroyed for solar energy developments on the premise of reducing carbon dioxide levels in the atmosphere. The long-term implications of disturbing desert soils need to be considered during every land use decision we make today. Scientific evidence suggests that the choices we make today to disturb desert ecosystems could continue to negatively impact these systems for thousands of years, even after the impacted area is mechanically restored upon site decommissioning.

Let us Choose to Keep our Desert Working for Us!

Are we doing more damage than good by destroying a perfect, self-perpetuating carbon storage system on undisturbed desert soils?

These groundbreaking discoveries are not new, just unseen; they have been dependably keeping our desert beautiful and healthy for millennia.

Although seemingly small in scale, the living processes that are occurring at the boundary between the atmosphere and our soil surface, as well as those special interactions happening at the boundary between the soil and plant roots, have a profound influence on the function of ecosystems at every level: local, landscape, regional, and global.

The desert's underground life-support systems can only keep functioning if the aboveground systems (desert plants and soil crusts) are kept alive and intact.

Wherever possible, we need to steer developments to pre-disturbed soil, parking lots, or roof tops. Then, we get the best of all options: progress with preservation.

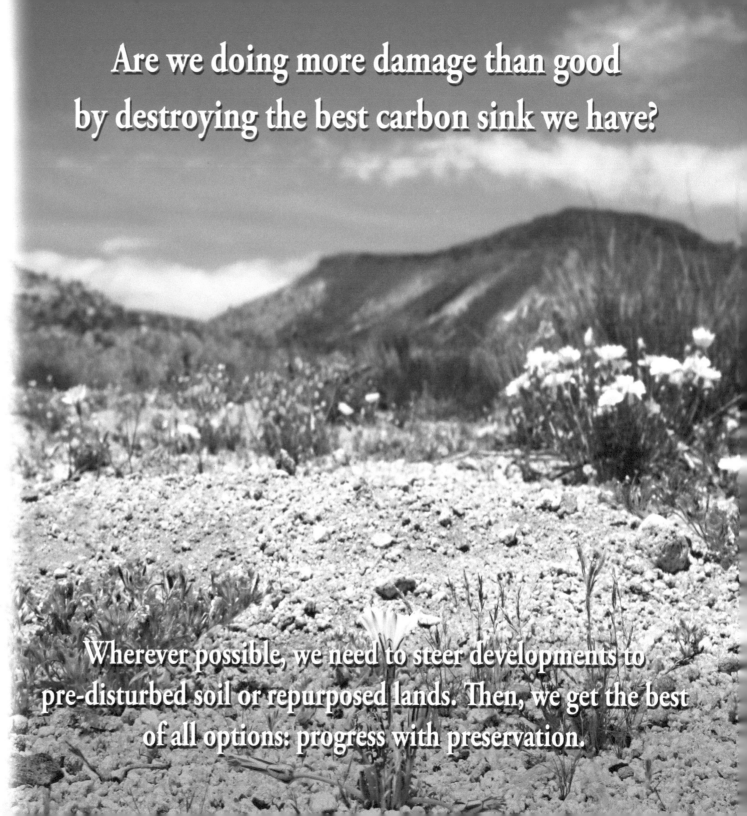

Let's choose to keep our desert working for us!

Are we doing more damage than good by destroying the best carbon sink we have?

These groundbreaking discoveries are not new, just unseen, silently keeping our desert beautiful and healthy for millennia.

The desert's underground life-support systems can only keep functioning if the aboveground systems are kept alive and intact.

Wherever possible, we need to steer developments to pre-disturbed soil or repurposed lands. Then, we get the best of all options: progress with preservation.

Leave our Hidden Soil Magicians Alone to Do Their Work

Our undisturbed desert will continue to protect and serve us as it has for millennia.

We must be their voice and their champion in protecting these critical microbes, plants, and soils – so they can continue to silently protect our potential for carbon sequestration and storage, our air quality, our health, our economy, our landscape, our ecotourism, our property values, and our quality of life.

To ensure our own sustainable future, we need to keep our desert soils intact and alive…it benefits *everyone.* The choice is ours.

"What a surprise that a landscape as seemingly stark as the desert, with apparently few practical uses, could actually be working every day to help us with major issues as critical as climate change! It does seem almost magical that tiny fungal threads that we walk over every day are protecting us from ourselves, invisibly making everything we see across the landscape more healthy and productive, and improving every aspect for life on Earth."

Robin

Leave our hidden soil magicians alone to do their work.
Our undisturbed desert will continue to protect and
serve us as it has for millennia.

Robin Kobaly

Author/Photography/Research/Graphics

Robin Kobaly is a botanist and plant ecologist with expertise in plant communities across the American southwest. She is Executive Director of The SummerTree Institute, and President and cofounder of The Power of Plants.

Kobaly has degrees from the University of California, Riverside (B.A. in Biology and M.A. in Plant Ecology), and four decades of experience in plant ecology, wildlife biology, land use management, aerial photo interpretation, and natural history interpretation. As a botanist for the U.S. Bureau of Land Management for 21 years, Kobaly worked on regional conservation plans, habitat management plans, management plans for Areas of Critical Environmental Concern (ACECs), and environmental impact statements. She has interpreted aerial photography to determine plant species composition, cover, biomass, and productivity desert-wide in California, and integrated satellite imagery, aerial photography, and ground data to help produce the vegetation map for the California Desert Conservation Area. Kobaly has worked with NASA's Jet Propulsion Laboratory to train scientists from NASA and BLM in new techniques for vegetation and soils mapping.

In addition, Kobaly has conducted inventories and monitored impacts to rare, threatened, and endangered plant species, and resolved conflicts between resource protection and human activities within "Watchable Wildlife Areas," wildlife preserves, and Areas of Critical Environmental Concern.

She was one of the co-founders of The Wildlands Conservancy, and served as preserve manager of Big Morongo Canyon Preserve for nine years. As preserve manager, Kobaly helped restore the site after a destructive fire, and constructed new full-access boardwalks, decks, and other facilities, developed an acclaimed environmental education program, and expanded the preserve from 3,600 to nearly 31,000 acres to protect critical habitat and link wildlife migration corridors.

One of Kobaly's passions is communicating environmental topics in terms everyone can understand. She has lectured extensively throughout the West, presenting seminars, classes, and workshops on issues ranging from water use in the changing western climate to ancient desert plants, living desert soils, ethnobotanical uses of native plants, the uniqueness of the desert biome, and how to sustainably use its resources. She incorporated her knowledge of drought-tolerant and southwest native plants into a four-hour interactive DVD, "Water-Wise Landscaping."

Kobaly recently served on the Independent Science Panel providing science-based input to the planning process for the Desert Renewable Energy Conservation Plan (DRECP), to advise state and federal agencies comprising the Renewable Energy Action Team (REAT) in guiding renewable energy development in the California desert.

She was awarded the 2018 Minerva Hoyt Conservation Award by the Joshua Tree National Park Association for her contributions to education, research, and preservation of the California desert. Kobaly helped lead the effort to form the newly designated Sand to Snow National Monument, connecting desert and montane habitats of the San Bernardino Mountains, southern Mojave Desert, and northwestern Colorado Desert.

Visit www.SummerTree.org and
www.PowerOfPlants.com to view her projects and programs.

Juniper Harrower

Artist for The Desert Underground

Dr. Juniper Harrower specializes in species interactions under climate change as both an ecologist and multimedia artist. Harrower founded SymbioArtlab, an environmental arts production company that contracts with national parks, universities, and the private sector to impact positive environmental change.

Harrower's research is published in both science and art scholarly journals and has shaped environmental policy. She is a National Science Foundation iCorps Fellow, an Oakland Teaching Fellow, and a Cota-Robles Fellow dedicated to advancing research for multicultural societies.

Her work is exhibited locally and internationally in galleries and museums, and her research and artistic products have received broad exposure in popular media such as National Geographic, the associated press, podcasts, music festivals and conferences.

Visit www.juniperharrower.com to view her online portfolio.

References

Abella SR (2010) Disturbance and Plant Succession in the Mojave and Sonoran Deserts of the American Southwest. Int J Environ Res Public Health 7(4): 12481284. Published online 2010 Mar 25. doi: 10.3390/ijerph7041248

Allen MF, Jenerette GD, Santiago LS (2013) Carbon Balance in California Deserts: Impacts of Widespread Solar Power Generation. California Energy Commission Publication number: CEC-500-2013-063

Allen MF, Barrows CW, Bell MD, Jenerette GD, Johnson RF, Allen EB (2014) Threats to California's Desert Ecosystems. Fremontia 42: 3-8

Belnap J, Hawkes CV, Firestone MK (2003) Boundaries in Miniature: Two Examples from Soil. BioScience 53(8): 739–749

Belnap J, Lange OL, eds. (2003) Biological Soil Crusts: Structure, Function, and Management. 2nd ed. Berlin: Springer-Verlag

Bloss, HE (1985) Studies of Symbiotic Microflora and Their Role in the Ecology of Desert Plants. Desert Plants 7: 119-127

Bowers JE, Webb RH, Rondeau RJ. (1995) Longevity, recruitment and mortality of desert plants in Grand Canyon, Arizona, USA. Journal of Vegetation Science 6(4): 551-564

Bowns JE, West NE (1976) Blackbrush (Coleogyne ramosissima Torr.) on southwestern Utah rangelands. Research Report 27. Utah Agricultural Experiment Station Logan, Utah, USA

Bucking, H, Mensah J, Fellbaum CR (2016) Common mycorrhizal networks and their effect on the bargaining power of the fungal partner in the arbuscular mycorrhizal symbiosis. Communicative Integrative Biology 9(1) e1107684

Christensen EM, Brown RC (1963) A blackbrush over 400 years old. Journal of Range Management 16: 118

Cody ML (2000) Slow-motion population dynamics in Mojave Desert perennial plants. Journal of Vegetation Science 11: 351–358

Comis D, (2002) Glomalin: Hiding Place for a Third of the World's Stored Soil Carbon. Agricultural Research Magazine Sept. 2002: 4-749

Evans RD, Koyama A, Sonderegger DL, Charlet TN, Newingham BA, Fenstermaker

LF, Harlow B, Jun VL, Ogle K, Smith SD, Nowak, RS (2014) Greater ecosystem carbon in the Mojave Desert after ten years exposure to elevated CO2. Nature Climate Change 4: 394–397

Francis R, Read DJ (1984) Direct transfer of carbon between plants connected by vesicular–arbuscular mycorrhizal mycelium. Nature 307: 53–56

Gibbens RP, Lenz JM (2001) Root Systems of some Chihuahuan Desert Plants. Journal of Arid Environments 49: 221-263

Gorzelak MA, Asay AK, Pickles BJ, Simard SW (2015) Inter-plant communication through mycorrhizal networks mediates complex adaptive behaviour in plant communities. AoB PLANTS, Volume 7, 1 January 2015

Green LE, Porras-Alfaro A, Sinsabaugh RL (2008) Translocation of Nitrogen and Carbon Integrates Biotic Crust and Grass Production in Desert Grassland. Journal of Ecology 96: 413-20

Hernandez RR, Hoffacker MK, Murphy-Mariscal ML, Wu G, and Allen MF (2015) Solar energy development impacts on land-cover change and protected areas. Proceedings of the National Academy of Sciences, USA 112: 13579-14584

Hernandez RR, Easter SB, Murphy-Mariscal ML, Maestre FT, Tavassoli M, Allen EB, Barrows CW, Belnap J, Ochoa-Hueso R, Ravi S, Allen MF (2014) Environmental impacts of utility-scale solar energy. Renewable and Sustainable Energy Reviews 29: 766-779

Jasoni RL, Smith SD, Arnone JA (2005) Net ecosystem CO2 exchange in Mojave Desert shrublands during the eighth year of exposure to elevated CO2. Global Change Biology 11: 749–756